WILSON®

just words®

Composition
Book

Wilson Language Training Corporation

www.wilsonlanguage.com

Name: _____

WILSON® Just Words® Student Composition Book

Item # JWSCB

ISBN # 978-1-56778-387-2

PUBLISHED BY:

Wilson Language Training Corporation
47 Old Webster Road
Oxford, MA 01540
United States of America

(800) 899-8454

www.wilsonlanguage.com

Printed in the U.S.A.

December 2022

UNIT 2

Day 5	Day 7

UNIT 3

Day 5	Day 7

UNIT 4

Day 5	Day 7

UNIT 5

Day 5	Day 7

MATCH SYLLABLES

1st Syllable	2nd Syllable	Word
rel	sult	_____
in	plex	_____
ton	test	_____
com	ish	_____
sub	ic	_____
cred	net	_____
mag	it	_____
con	mit	_____
buck	et	_____

BONUS UNIT I

Day 1	Day 3

BONUS UNIT I

Day 4	Day 5

MATCH ROOT WITH MEANING

Root	Meaning	Example
fract	throw	_____
fect	break	_____
ject	make	_____
junct	small	_____
min	join	_____
struct	write	_____
tox	choose	_____
lect	drag	_____
scrib	build	_____
tract	poison	_____

UNIT 6

Day 5	Day 7

UNIT 7

Day 5	Day 7

UNIT 8

Day 5	Day 7

MATCH SYLLABLE

1st Syllable	2nd Syllable	Word
re	line	_____
lo	nate	_____
sky	cate	_____
do	zen	_____
fro	cline	_____

BONUS UNIT II

Day 1	Day 3

BONUS UNIT II

Day 4	Day 5

MATCH PREFIX WITH ROOT

Prefix	Root	Word
de	vide	_____
re	quate	_____
e	dict	_____
pre	tox	_____
pro	ject	_____

UNIT 9

Day 5	Day 7

UNIT 10

Day 5	Day 7

MATCH SYLLABLES

1st Syllable	2nd Syllable	Word
ar	dy	_____
par	port	_____
gar	my	_____
dis	y	_____
glor	lic	_____
for	tort	_____
de	ty	_____
tar	bid	_____

UNIT 11

Day 5	Day 7

UNIT 12

Day 5	Day 7

UNIT 13

Day 5	Day 7

UNIT 14

Day 3	**Day 5**

Day 7	**Day 8**

THIS PAGE IS INTENTIONALLY LEFT BLANK

SOUNDS

1 _____ 2 _____ 3 _____

WORDS

Review

1 _____

2 _____

Nonsense

1 _____

2 _____

Current

1 _____

2 _____

3 _____

4 _____

5 _____

6 _____

PHRASES

1 _____

2 _____

3 _____

4 _____

SENTENCES

1 _____

2 _____

Dictation

SOUNDS

1 _____   2 _____   3 _____

WORDS

Review

Nonsense

1 _____   1 _____

2 _____   2 _____

Current

1 _____   4 _____

2 _____   5 _____

3 _____   6 _____

PHRASES

1 _____   3 _____

2 _____   4 _____

SENTENCES

1 _____

2 _____

SOUNDS

1 _____ 2 _____ 3 _____

WORDS

Review

1 _____

2 _____

Nonsense

1 _____

2 _____

Current

1 _____

2 _____

3 _____

4 _____

5 _____

6 _____

PHRASES

1 _____

2 _____

3 _____

4 _____

SENTENCES

1 _____

2 _____

SOUNDS

1 _____ 2 _____ 3 _____

WORDS

Review

1 _____

2 _____

Current

1 _____

2 _____

3 _____

Nonsense

1 _____

2 _____

4 _____

5 _____

6 _____

PHRASES

1 _____

2 _____

3 _____

4 _____

SENTENCES

1 _____

2 _____

SOUNDS

1 _____   2 _____   3 _____

WORDS

Review

1 _____

2 _____

Nonsense

1 _____

2 _____

Current

1 _____

2 _____

3 _____

4 _____

5 _____

6 _____

PHRASES

1 _____

2 _____

3 _____

4 _____

SENTENCES

1 _____

2 _____

SOUNDS

1 _____ 2 _____ 3 _____

WORDS

Review

1 _____

2 _____

Nonsense

1 _____

2 _____

Current

1 _____

2 _____

3 _____

4 _____

5 _____

6 _____

PHRASES

1 _____

2 _____

3 _____

4 _____

SENTENCES

1 _____

2 _____

SOUNDS

1 _____ 2 _____ 3 _____

WORDS

Review

1 _____

2 _____

Nonsense

1 _____

2 _____

Current

1 _____

2 _____

3 _____

4 _____

5 _____

6 _____

PHRASES

1 _____

2 _____

3 _____

4 _____

SENTENCES

1 _____

2 _____

SOUNDS

1 _____ 2 _____ 3 _____

WORDS

Review

1 _____

2 _____

Nonsense

1 _____

2 _____

Current

1 _____

2 _____

3 _____

4 _____

5 _____

6 _____

PHRASES

1 _____

2 _____

3 _____

4 _____

SENTENCES

1 _____

2 _____

SOUNDS

1 _____ 2 _____ 3 _____

WORDS

Review

1 _____

2 _____

Nonsense

1 _____

2 _____

Current

1 _____

2 _____

3 _____

4 _____

5 _____

6 _____

PHRASES

1 _____

2 _____

3 _____

4 _____

SENTENCES

1 _____

2 _____

SOUNDS

1 _____   2 _____   3 _____

WORDS

Review

1 _____

2 _____

Nonsense

1 _____

2 _____

Current

1 _____

2 _____

3 _____

4 _____

5 _____

6 _____

PHRASES

1 _____

2 _____

3 _____

4 _____

SENTENCES

1 _____

2 _____

SOUNDS

1 _____ 2 _____ 3 _____

WORDS

Review

1 _____

2 _____

Nonsense

1 _____

2 _____

Current

1 _____

2 _____

3 _____

4 _____

5 _____

6 _____

PHRASES

1 _____

2 _____

3 _____

4 _____

SENTENCES

1 _____

2 _____

SOUNDS

1 _____ 2 _____ 3 _____

WORDS

Review

1 _____

2 _____

Nonsense

1 _____

2 _____

Current

1 _____

2 _____

3 _____

4 _____

5 _____

6 _____

PHRASES

1 _____

2 _____

3 _____

4 _____

SENTENCES

1 _____

2 _____

SOUNDS

1 _____   2 _____   3 _____

WORDS

Review

1 _____

2 _____

Nonsense

1 _____

2 _____

Current

1 _____

2 _____

3 _____

4 _____

5 _____

6 _____

PHRASES

1 _____

2 _____

3 _____

4 _____

SENTENCES

1 _____

2 _____

SOUNDS

1 _____ 2 _____ 3 _____

WORDS

Review   Nonsense

1 _____   1 _____

2 _____   2 _____

Current

1 _____   4 _____

2 _____   5 _____

3 _____   6 _____

PHRASES

1 _____   3 _____

2 _____   4 _____

SENTENCES

1 _____

2 _____

SOUNDS

1 _____   2 _____   3 _____

WORDS

Review

1 _____

2 _____

Nonsense

1 _____

2 _____

Current

1 _____   4 _____

2 _____   5 _____

3 _____   6 _____

PHRASES

1 _____   3 _____

2 _____   4 _____

SENTENCES

1 _____

2 _____

SOUNDS

1 _____ 2 _____ 3 _____

WORDS

Review

1 _____

2 _____

Nonsense

1 _____

2 _____

Current

1 _____

2 _____

3 _____

4 _____

5 _____

6 _____

PHRASES

1 _____

2 _____

3 _____

4 _____

SENTENCES

1 _____

2 _____

SOUNDS

1 _____ 2 _____ 3 _____

WORDS

Review

1 _____

2 _____

Nonsense

1 _____

2 _____

Current

1 _____

2 _____

3 _____

4 _____

5 _____

6 _____

PHRASES

1 _____

2 _____

3 _____

4 _____

SENTENCES

1 _____

2 _____

SOUNDS

1 _____ 2 _____ 3 _____

WORDS

Review

1 _____

2 _____

Current

1 _____

2 _____

3 _____

Nonsense

1 _____

2 _____

4 _____

5 _____

6 _____

PHRASES

1 _____ 3 _____

2 _____ 4 _____

SENTENCES

1 _____

2 _____

SOUNDS

1 _____ 2 _____ 3 _____

WORDS

Review

1 _____

2 _____

Nonsense

1 _____

2 _____

Current

1 _____

2 _____

3 _____

4 _____

5 _____

6 _____

PHRASES

1 _____

2 _____

3 _____

4 _____

SENTENCES

1 _____

2 _____

SOUNDS

1 _____ 2 _____ 3 _____

WORDS

Review

1 _____

2 _____

Nonsense

1 _____

2 _____

Current

1 _____

2 _____

3 _____

4 _____

5 _____

6 _____

PHRASES

1 _____

2 _____

3 _____

4 _____

SENTENCES

1 _____

2 _____

SOUNDS

1 _____ 2 _____ 3 _____

WORDS

Review   Nonsense

1 _____   1 _____

2 _____   2 _____

Current

1 _____   4 _____

2 _____   5 _____

3 _____   6 _____

PHRASES

1 _____   3 _____

2 _____   4 _____

SENTENCES

1 _____

2 _____

SOUNDS

1 _____   2 _____   3 _____

WORDS

Review   Nonsense

1 _____   1 _____

2 _____   2 _____

Current

1 _____   4 _____

2 _____   5 _____

3 _____   6 _____

PHRASES

1 _____   3 _____

2 _____   4 _____

SENTENCES

1 _____

2 _____

SOUNDS

1 _____ 2 _____ 3 _____

WORDS

Review   Nonsense

1 _____   1 _____

2 _____   2 _____

Current

1 _____   4 _____

2 _____   5 _____

3 _____   6 _____

PHRASES

1 _____   3 _____

2 _____   4 _____

SENTENCES

1 _____

2 _____

SOUNDS

1 _____ 2 _____ 3 _____

WORDS

Review

1 _____

2 _____

Nonsense

1 _____

2 _____

Current

1 _____

2 _____

3 _____

4 _____

5 _____

6 _____

PHRASES

1 _____

2 _____

3 _____

4 _____

SENTENCES

1 _____

2 _____

SOUNDS

1 _____ 2 _____ 3 _____

WORDS

Review

1 _____

2 _____

Nonsense

1 _____

2 _____

Current

1 _____

2 _____

3 _____

4 _____

5 _____

6 _____

PHRASES

1 _____

2 _____

3 _____

4 _____

SENTENCES

1 _____

2 _____

SOUNDS

1 _____ 2 _____ 3 _____

WORDS

Review

1 _____

2 _____

Nonsense

1 _____

2 _____

Current

1 _____

2 _____

3 _____

4 _____

5 _____

6 _____

PHRASES

1 _____

2 _____

3 _____

4 _____

SENTENCES

1 _____

2 _____

SOUNDS

1 _____   2 _____   3 _____

WORDS

Review

1 _____

2 _____

Nonsense

1 _____

2 _____

Current

1 _____

2 _____

3 _____

4 _____

5 _____

6 _____

PHRASES

1 _____

2 _____

3 _____

4 _____

SENTENCES

1 _____

2 _____

SOUNDS

1 _____ 2 _____ 3 _____

WORDS

Review

1 _____

2 _____

Nonsense

1 _____

2 _____

Current

1 _____

2 _____

3 _____

4 _____

5 _____

6 _____

PHRASES

1 _____

2 _____

3 _____

4 _____

SENTENCES

1 _____

2 _____

SOUNDS

1 _____   2 _____   3 _____

WORDS

Review

1 _____

2 _____

Current

1 _____

2 _____

3 _____

Nonsense

1 _____

2 _____

4 _____

5 _____

6 _____

PHRASES

1 _____

2 _____

3 _____

4 _____

SENTENCES

1 _____

2 _____

SOUNDS

1 _____ 2 _____ 3 _____

WORDS

Review

1 _____

2 _____

Nonsense

1 _____

2 _____

Current

1 _____

2 _____

3 _____

4 _____

5 _____

6 _____

PHRASES

1 _____

2 _____

3 _____

4 _____

SENTENCES

1 _____

2 _____

SOUNDS

1 _____ 2 _____ 3 _____

WORDS

Review

1 _____

2 _____

Nonsense

1 _____

2 _____

Current

1 _____

2 _____

3 _____

4 _____

5 _____

6 _____

PHRASES

1 _____

2 _____

3 _____

4 _____

SENTENCES

1 _____

_____

2 _____

SOUNDS

1 _____   2 _____   3 _____

WORDS

Review

1 _____

2 _____

Nonsense

1 _____

2 _____

Current

1 _____

2 _____

3 _____

4 _____

5 _____

6 _____

PHRASES

1 _____

2 _____

3 _____

4 _____

SENTENCES

1 _____

2 _____

SOUNDS

1 _____ 2 _____ 3 _____

WORDS

Review

1 _____

2 _____

Nonsense

1 _____

2 _____

Current

1 _____

2 _____

3 _____

4 _____

5 _____

6 _____

PHRASES

1 _____

2 _____

3 _____

4 _____

SENTENCES

1 _____

2 _____

SOUNDS

1 _____   2 _____   3 _____

WORDS

Review

Nonsense

1 _____   1 _____

2 _____   2 _____

Current

1 _____   4 _____

2 _____   5 _____

3 _____   6 _____

PHRASES

1 _____   3 _____

2 _____   4 _____

SENTENCES

1 _____

2 _____

SOUNDS

1 _____ 2 _____ 3 _____

WORDS

Review

1 _____

2 _____

Nonsense

1 _____

2 _____

Current

1 _____

2 _____

3 _____

4 _____

5 _____

6 _____

PHRASES

1 _____

2 _____

3 _____

4 _____

SENTENCES

1 _____

2 _____

SOUNDS

1 _____   2 _____   3 _____

WORDS

Review

1 _____

2 _____

Nonsense

1 _____

2 _____

Current

1 _____

2 _____

3 _____

4 _____

5 _____

6 _____

PHRASES

1 _____

2 _____

3 _____

4 _____

SENTENCES

1 _____

2 _____

SOUNDS

1 _____ 2 _____ 3 _____

WORDS

Review

1 _____

2 _____

Nonsense

1 _____

2 _____

Current

1 _____

2 _____

3 _____

4 _____

5 _____

6 _____

PHRASES

1 _____

2 _____

3 _____

4 _____

SENTENCES

1 _____

2 _____

SOUNDS

1 _____ 2 _____ 3 _____

WORDS

Review

1 _____

2 _____

Current

1 _____

2 _____

3 _____

Nonsense

1 _____

2 _____

4 _____

5 _____

6 _____

PHRASES

1 _____

2 _____

3 _____

4 _____

SENTENCES

1 _____

2 _____

SOUNDS

1 _____ 2 _____ 3 _____

WORDS

Review

1 _____

2 _____

Nonsense

1 _____

2 _____

Current

1 _____

2 _____

3 _____

4 _____

5 _____

6 _____

PHRASES

1 _____

2 _____

3 _____

4 _____

SENTENCES

1 _____

2 _____

SOUNDS

1 _____   2 _____   3 _____

WORDS

Review

1 _____

2 _____

Nonsense

1 _____

2 _____

Current

1 _____

2 _____

3 _____

4 _____

5 _____

6 _____

PHRASES

1 _____

2 _____

3 _____

4 _____

SENTENCES

1 _____

2 _____

SOUNDS

1 _____   2 _____   3 _____

WORDS

Review   Nonsense

1 _____   1 _____

2 _____   2 _____

Current

1 _____   4 _____

2 _____   5 _____

3 _____   6 _____

PHRASES

1 _____   3 _____

2 _____   4 _____

SENTENCES

1 _____

2 _____

SOUNDS

1 _____   2 _____   3 _____

WORDS

Review

1 _____

2 _____

Nonsense

1 _____

2 _____

Current

1 _____

2 _____

3 _____

4 _____

5 _____

6 _____

PHRASES

1 _____

2 _____

3 _____

4 _____

SENTENCES

1 _____

2 _____

SOUNDS

1 _____   2 _____   3 _____

WORDS

Review   Nonsense

1 _____   1 _____

2 _____   2 _____

Current

1 _____   4 _____

2 _____   5 _____

3 _____   6 _____

PHRASES

1 _____   3 _____

2 _____   4 _____

SENTENCES

1 _____

2 _____

SOUNDS

1 _____   2 _____   3 _____

WORDS

Review   Nonsense

1 _____   1 _____

2 _____   2 _____

Current

1 _____   4 _____

2 _____   5 _____

3 _____   6 _____

PHRASES

1 _____   3 _____

2 _____   4 _____

SENTENCES

1 _____

2 _____

SOUNDS

1 _____ 2 _____ 3 _____

WORDS

Review

1 _____

2 _____

Nonsense

1 _____

2 _____

Current

1 _____

2 _____

3 _____

4 _____

5 _____

6 _____

PHRASES

1 _____

2 _____

3 _____

4 _____

SENTENCES

1 _____

2 _____

SOUNDS

1 _____ 2 _____ 3 _____

WORDS

Review   Nonsense

1 _____   1 _____

2 _____   2 _____

Current

1 _____   4 _____

2 _____   5 _____

3 _____   6 _____

PHRASES

1 _____   3 _____

2 _____   4 _____

SENTENCES

1 _____

2 _____

SOUNDS

1 _____   2 _____   3 _____

WORDS

Review   Nonsense

1 _____   1 _____

2 _____   2 _____

Current

1 _____   4 _____

2 _____   5 _____

3 _____   6 _____

PHRASES

1 _____   3 _____

2 _____   4 _____

SENTENCES

1 _____

2 _____

SOUNDS

1 _____   2 _____   3 _____

WORDS

Review

1 _____

2 _____

Nonsense

1 _____

2 _____

Current

1 _____

2 _____

3 _____

4 _____

5 _____

6 _____

PHRASES

1 _____

2 _____

3 _____

4 _____

SENTENCES

1 _____

2 _____

SOUNDS

1 _____ 2 _____ 3 _____

WORDS

Review

1 _____

2 _____

Nonsense

1 _____

2 _____

Current

1 _____

2 _____

3 _____

4 _____

5 _____

6 _____

PHRASES

1 _____

2 _____

3 _____

4 _____

SENTENCES

1 _____

2 _____

SOUNDS

1 _____ 2 _____ 3 _____

WORDS

Review

1 _____

2 _____

Nonsense

1 _____

2 _____

Current

1 _____

2 _____

3 _____

4 _____

5 _____

6 _____

PHRASES

1 _____

2 _____

3 _____

4 _____

SENTENCES

1 _____

2 _____

SOUNDS

1 _____ 2 _____ 3 _____

WORDS

Review

1 _____

2 _____

Nonsense

1 _____

2 _____

Current

1 _____

2 _____

3 _____

4 _____

5 _____

6 _____

PHRASES

1 _____

2 _____

3 _____

4 _____

SENTENCES

1 _____

2 _____

SOUNDS

1 _____ 2 _____ 3 _____

WORDS

Review   Nonsense

1 _____   1 _____

2 _____   2 _____

Current

1 _____   4 _____

2 _____   5 _____

3 _____   6 _____

PHRASES

1 _____   3 _____

2 _____   4 _____

SENTENCES

1 _____

2 _____

SOUNDS

1 _____   2 _____   3 _____

WORDS

Review

1 _____

2 _____

Nonsense

1 _____

2 _____

Current

1 _____

2 _____

3 _____

4 _____

5 _____

6 _____

PHRASES

1 _____

2 _____

3 _____

4 _____

SENTENCES

1 _____

2 _____

SOUNDS

1 _____   2 _____   3 _____

WORDS

Review

1 _____

2 _____

Nonsense

1 _____

2 _____

Current

1 _____

2 _____

3 _____

4 _____

5 _____

6 _____

PHRASES

1 _____

2 _____

3 _____

4 _____

SENTENCES

1 _____

2 _____

SOUNDS

1 _____ 2 _____ 3 _____

WORDS

Review

1 _____

2 _____

Current

1 _____

2 _____

3 _____

Nonsense

1 _____

2 _____

4 _____

5 _____

6 _____

PHRASES

1 _____

2 _____

3 _____

4 _____

SENTENCES

1 _____

2 _____

SOUNDS

1 _____ 2 _____ 3 _____

WORDS

Review

1 _____

2 _____

Nonsense

1 _____

2 _____

Current

1 _____

2 _____

3 _____

4 _____

5 _____

6 _____

PHRASES

1 _____

2 _____

3 _____

4 _____

SENTENCES

1 _____

2 _____

SOUNDS

1 _____   2 _____   3 _____

WORDS

Review

1 _____

2 _____

Nonsense

1 _____

2 _____

Current

1 _____

2 _____

3 _____

4 _____

5 _____

6 _____

PHRASES

1 _____   3 _____

2 _____   4 _____

SENTENCES

1 _____

2 _____

SOUNDS

1 _____ 2 _____ 3 _____

WORDS

Review

1 _____

2 _____

Nonsense

1 _____

2 _____

Current

1 _____

2 _____

3 _____

4 _____

5 _____

6 _____

PHRASES

1 _____

2 _____

3 _____

4 _____

SENTENCES

1 _____

2 _____

SOUNDS

1 _____ 2 _____ 3 _____

WORDS

Review

1 _____

2 _____

Current

1 _____

2 _____

3 _____

Nonsense

1 _____

2 _____

4 _____

5 _____

6 _____

PHRASES

1 _____

2 _____

3 _____

4 _____

SENTENCES

1 _____

2 _____

SOUNDS

1 _____ 2 _____ 3 _____

WORDS

Review

1 _____

2 _____

Nonsense

1 _____

2 _____

Current

1 _____

2 _____

3 _____

4 _____

5 _____

6 _____

PHRASES

1 _____

2 _____

3 _____

4 _____

SENTENCES

1 _____

2 _____

SOUNDS

1 _____ 2 _____ 3 _____

WORDS

Review

1 _____

2 _____

Nonsense

1 _____

2 _____

Current

1 _____

2 _____

3 _____

4 _____

5 _____

6 _____

PHRASES

1 _____

2 _____

3 _____

4 _____

SENTENCES

1 _____

2 _____

SOUNDS

1 _____ 2 _____ 3 _____

WORDS

Review

1 _____

2 _____

Nonsense

1 _____

2 _____

Current

1 _____

2 _____

3 _____

4 _____

5 _____

6 _____

PHRASES

1 _____

2 _____

3 _____

4 _____

SENTENCES

1 _____

2 _____

SOUNDS

1 _____ 2 _____ 3 _____

WORDS

Review   Nonsense

1 _____   1 _____

2 _____   2 _____

Current

1 _____   4 _____

2 _____   5 _____

3 _____   6 _____

PHRASES

1 _____   3 _____

2 _____   4 _____

SENTENCES

1 _____

2 _____

SOUNDS

1 _____   2 _____   3 _____

WORDS

Review

1 _____

2 _____

Nonsense

1 _____

2 _____

Current

1 _____

2 _____

3 _____

4 _____

5 _____

6 _____

PHRASES

1 _____

2 _____

3 _____

4 _____

SENTENCES

1 _____

2 _____

SOUNDS

1 _____ 2 _____ 3 _____

WORDS

Review

Nonsense

1 _____

1 _____

2 _____

2 _____

Current

1 _____

4 _____

2 _____

5 _____

3 _____

6 _____

PHRASES

1 _____

3 _____

2 _____

4 _____

SENTENCES

1 _____

2 _____

SOUNDS

1 _____   2 _____   3 _____

WORDS

Review

1 _____

2 _____

Current

1 _____

2 _____

3 _____

Nonsense

1 _____

2 _____

4 _____

5 _____

6 _____

PHRASES

1 _____

2 _____

3 _____

4 _____

SENTENCES

1 _____

2 _____

NOTES

NOTES